Smashin'!

THIS EDITION PUBLISHED 2012 BY
WAVERLEY BOOKS,
144 PORT DUNDAS ROAD,
GLASGOW, G4 0HZ

OOR WULLIE IS COPYRIGHT © AND REGISTERED
® 2012, DC THOMSON & CO LTD
FIRST PUBLISHED 2012

ISBN 978-1-84934-108-0

PRINTED AND BOUND
IN ITALY.

A-MAZE-ING!

Can you make it a hole in one?

A-MAZE-ING!

This maze will lead you to a strike!

EAGLE EYED!

These eagle pictures may look alike, but can you spot the odd one out?

A

B

C

D

Question of Sport!

Darts

Swimming

Rounders

Snooker

Tennis

EACH PICTURE REPRESENTS A WORD THAT IS LINKED WITH A PARTICULAR SPORT. CAN YOU IDENTIFY THE WORDS, THEN MATCH THEM TO THE SPORTS IN THE LIST?

ANSWERS: Darts–Bull, Swimming–Butterfly, Rounders–Bat, Snooker–Pocket, Tennis–Ace.

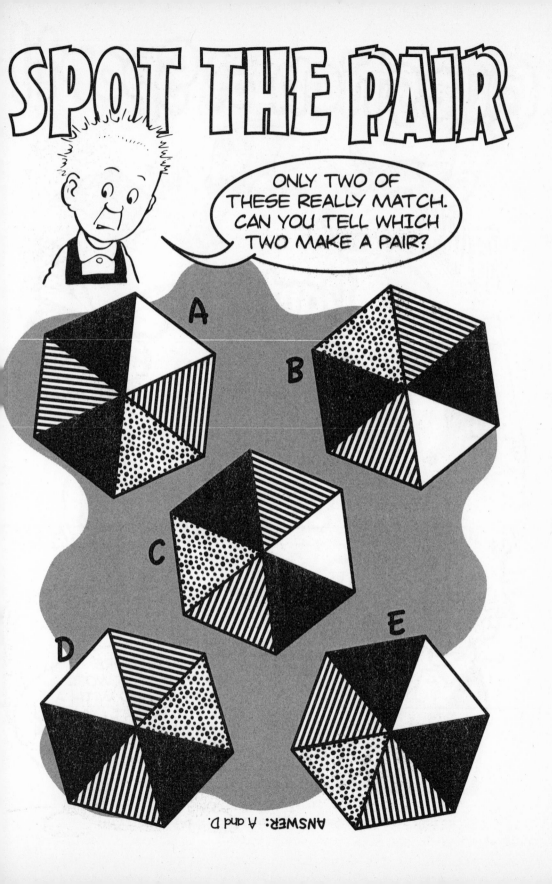

A-MAZE-ING!

Wullie's thought up a game for you and a pal to play. Starting at point X, trace along the line, taking whichever route you choose, and see who is first to score a goal. If you come to a "Tackled" marker, then it's time for your opponent's turn.

CROSS-COUNTRY RUN

Wullie and the gang are late for tea. Taking a shortcut they must get home by going through each neighbour's gate only once. (The numbers beside the gates are not in the correct order for the solution.) Can you find the right path?

Start

1

4

3

2

5
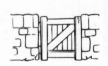

6

8

7
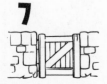

Finish

ANSWER: 1, 2, 7, 6, 3, 4, 5, 8.

OOR WULLIE FUN SECTION

Jim — "I've just had dinner at that new restaurant in town."
Joe — "What was it like?"
Jim — "The food was fine, but the bill was a bit hard to swallow!"

Sergeant — "And does the suspect have a record?"
Police officer — "No, sergeant, but he has quite a large CD collection!"

Pupil — "Can you send my exam results to my parents by e-mail, please, miss?"
Teacher — "But you don't have a computer at home, Jimmy!"
Pupil — "That's right, miss!"

Will — "I've invented a truth drink — would you like a taste?"
Bill — "Ugh! That tastes terrible!"
Will — "Ain't that the truth!"

WORDSEARCH

Find the birds I've seen and tried to feed in the wordsearch below.

```
B L A C K B I R D H B N A W S
K C O N N U D N C R E P P I D
W C H A F F I N C H R S V W L
E L G A E T I T O E O N T E K
H D H W R F O L D Y S P I R D
E O R A N R C N I P A T P E G
R V M E R T A M A A A J I L L
O E E A H S K R A K T Q P B O
N R P W O S R R C O B G U R V
G U J O Q O I O A W C D A A E
O B G D W R C F N L G R E W B
H C N I F D L O G I Y K O Q I
X S W A L L O W E N B K C W R
D I S T A R L I N G I O S U D
P X G N I T N U B C R K R P D
```

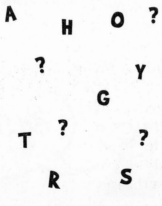

A
H O ?
?
Y
G
T ? ?
R S

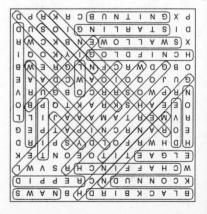

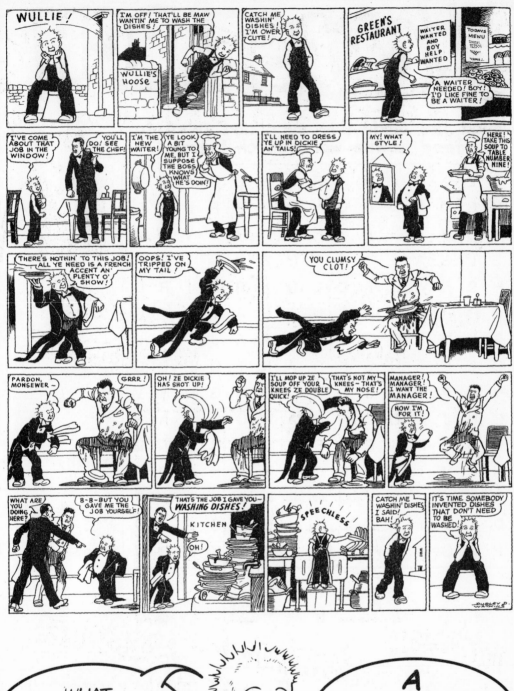

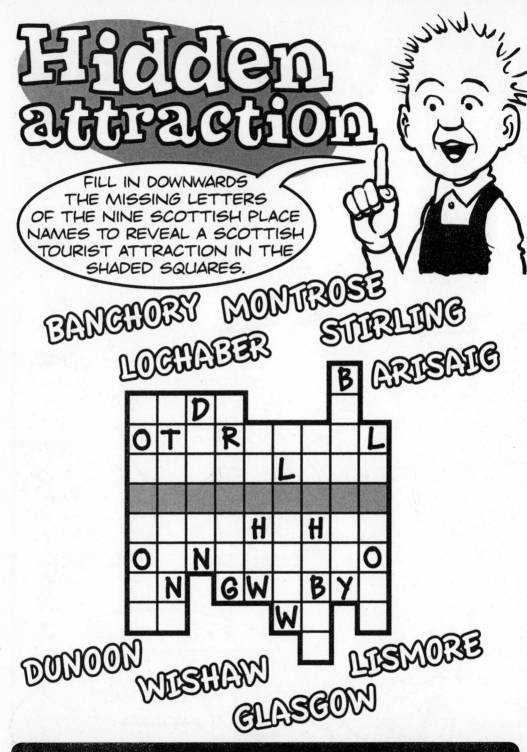

Hidden attraction

FILL IN DOWNWARDS THE MISSING LETTERS OF THE NINE SCOTTISH PLACE NAMES TO REVEAL A SCOTTISH TOURIST ATTRACTION IN THE SHADED SQUARES.

BANCHORY MONTROSE STIRLING

LOCHABER ARISAIG

DUNOON WISHAW LISMORE GLASGOW

Mouse trap

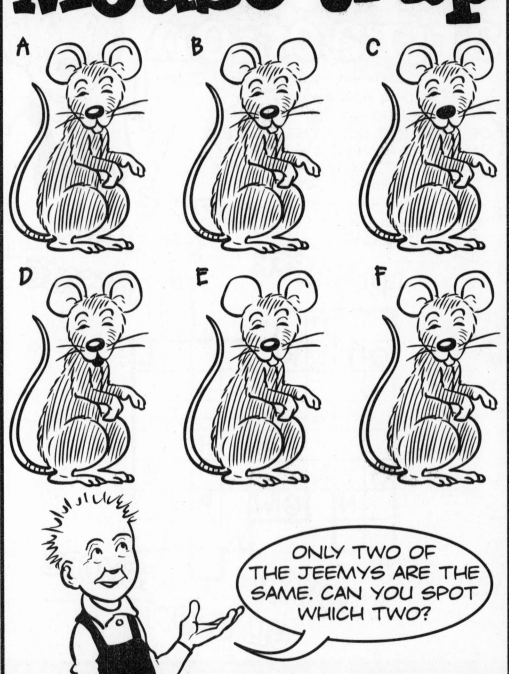

MY VERY OWN
Tartan

Design your own tartan in the frame
and write your name in the box below.

LOOK again

There are fifteen differences between these two pictures. How many can you find?

MUSIC
TO MY EARS

Can you write in eleven musical instruments, reading across, to complete this musical crossword? We've given some clues.

FISH FINDER!

NO FISHING

Start from certain letters and move from square to square in any direction to spell the names of at least 14 fish.

H	K	I	P	O	N	O
E	C	R	E	B	L	M
A	O	D	A	H	A	I
R	U	D	T	S	B	E
T	A	Y	S	U	E	L

ALL CHANGE!

PIT

WINCE

FIST

SHIPS

HURRY

ANSWER: PIE, MINCE, FISH, CHIPS, CURRY.

STEP WORDS

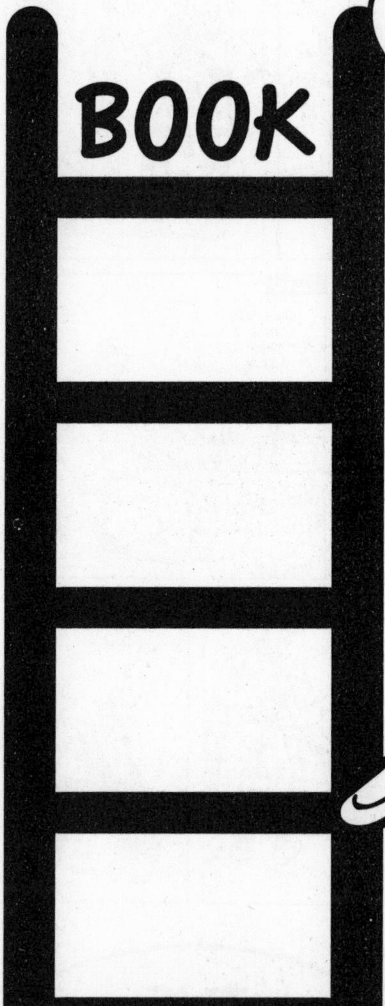

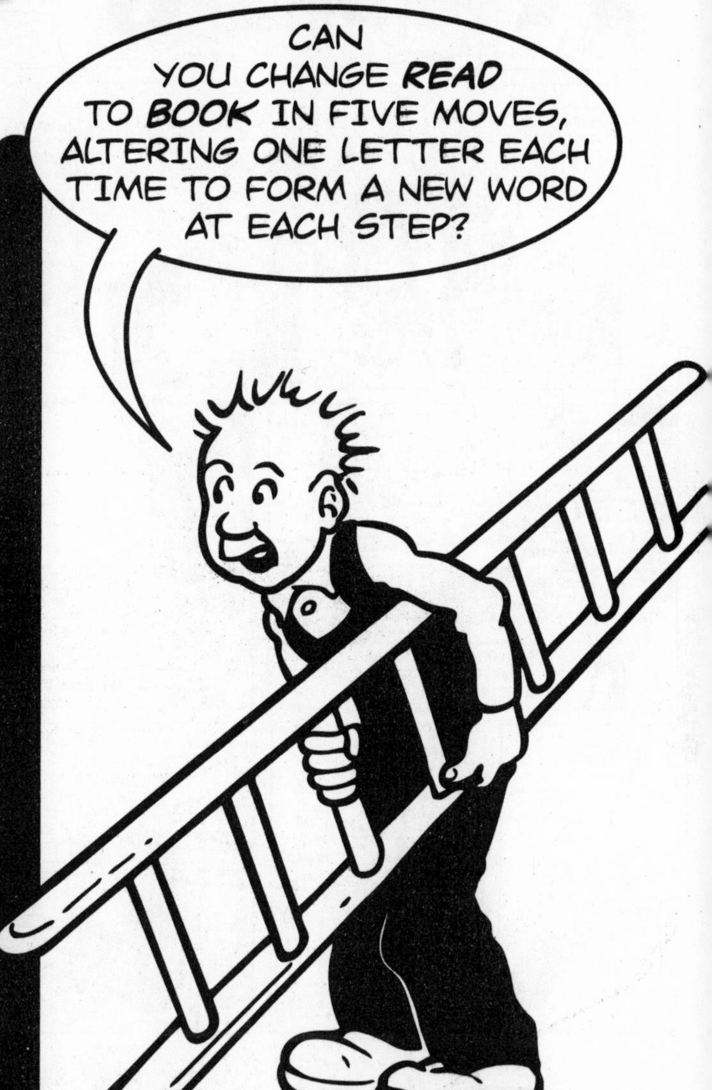

ANSWER: BOOK, BOOM, ROOM, ROAM, ROAD, READ.

MAKING WORDS

How many words of three letters or more can you make from this word?

hairstyle

WHAT'S IN A NAME?

Print a boy's name reading across to finish off seven boy's names reading downwards.

	G				
G	D	O			E
R	A	R	B	S	D
E	I	O	I	A	A
M	E	N	A	N	R
E	L		N		D

MUXED IP!

These Scottish city names have got all mixed up. Can you help Wullie sort them?

ABERDEE
DUNNESS
EDINDEEN INVERBURGH

WORD SQUARE

A word square contains words that read the same across and down. Use the list of words to make two word squares each containing the word EGGS.

DREW **GOAL**

EGGS **RAGE**

EGGS **SLAP**

GALA **WEST**

WATER BOTHER!

Which wheel should Wullie turn to stop the dripping tap?

ANSWER: C.

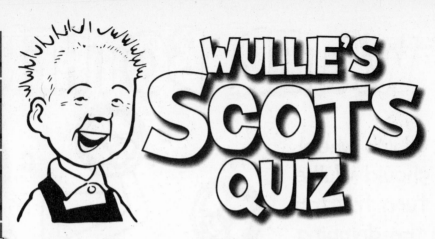

WULLIE'S SCOTS QUIZ

1 Which famous battle took place in June 1314?

2 Which football club plays at Pittodrie Stadium?

3 What colour are Aberdeen Angus cattle?

4 Which city is the Scott Monument in?

5 Which Fife town's name (which is notoriously difficult to say) means "The place of the wild boar"?

6 What are Corbetts?

7 What is traditionally put on porridge before it is eaten?

8 The caber toss features in what kind of event?

9 Which food does Burns describe as "great chieftain o' the puddin-race!"?

10 Which legendary cannibal is said to have lived with his 'clan' in a cave in Ayrshire in the 16th century?

ANSWERS: 1. Bannockburn. 2. Aberdeen. 3. Black. 4. Edinburgh. 5. Auchtermuchty. 6. Scottish mountains between 2500 and 3000 feet tall. 7. Salt (not sugar!). 8. Highland Games. 9. Haggis. 10. Sawney Bean.

FOOD SCRAMBLE

Can you unscramble the words around the crossword below to spell out famous Scottish dishes? If you're right, they should fit into the crossword grid (a few letters have been put in to help you). Once they're written in, a new Scottish food will be revealed in the shaded squares.

CHOTCS
THORB
CESNOS
SESVOTI
ACKLB
NUB
RIKIESL
ULLCEN
KINKS
PSAB
DIROPREG
LABLS
HOUDG
DEARBERGING

FUN FAIR WORDSEARCH

All the words listed below can be found in the wordsearch. You may read them up, down, backwards, forwards or diagonally. When you have found all the words, the letters in bold, reading from top to bottom, will give you another two fun fair rides.

CAROUSEL, LUCKY DIP, GHOST TRAIN, BIG DIPPER, BOUNCY CASTLE, ROLLER COASTER.

R	O	L	L	E	R	C	**W**
A	L	Y	C	N	U	O	B
L	E	S	U	O	R	A	C
U	**T**	**Z**	G	H	O	S	T
C	**E**	N	I	A	R	T	**R**
K	**S**	**D**	B	**O**	**D**	E	**G**
Y	D	I	P	P	E	R	**E**
E	L	T	S	A	C	**M**	**S**

HIDDEN SENTENCE

Try to spell out a four-word sentence. Start from a certain letter and move along a line to the next letter in any direction. Use each letter only once.

PURR

A SECRET MESSAGE

If you intercepted this secret message could you read it? It's quite simple really ... just hold it upside down in front of a mirror.

TELL NO ONE!
FOR THE NIGHT.
EMERGENCY RATIONS
BRING SOME
PROMPT TONIGHT,
AT NINE O'CLOCK
IN THE TOOLSHED
WILL MEET YOU

IN A JAM!

Wullie has been helping Ma make jam. Trouble is, the letters on the labels are all jumbled up. Can you unscramble them to find the five kinds of jam?

BHUARBR **PAHEC**

MULP **YERCHR**

NABNAA

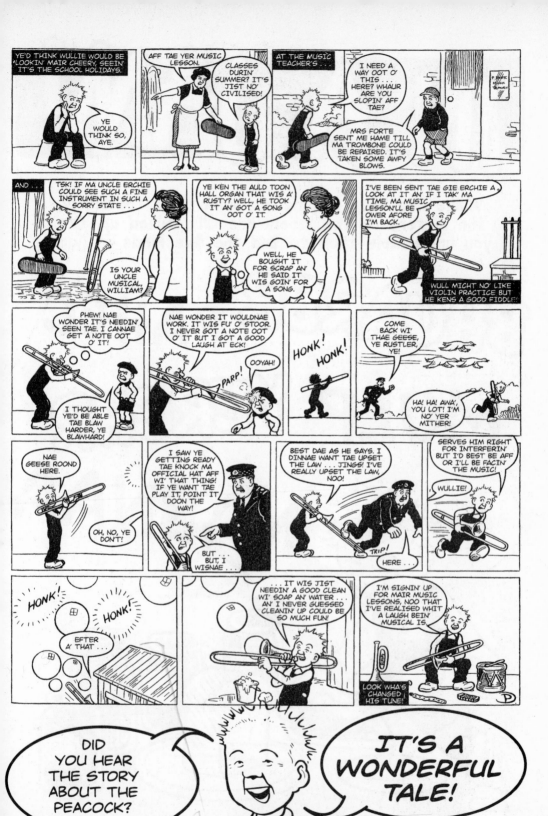

WULLIE'S PICTURE WORDS

Across

Down

MY CROSSWORD USES DRAWINGS INSTEAD OF WORDS FOR CLUES. CAN YOU SOLVE IT?

LOOK again ?

ONLY TWO OF THESE PICTURES OF WULLIE ARE IDENTICAL. **CAN YOU FIND THEM?**

ANSWER: 2 AND 5.

Hidden Scotland

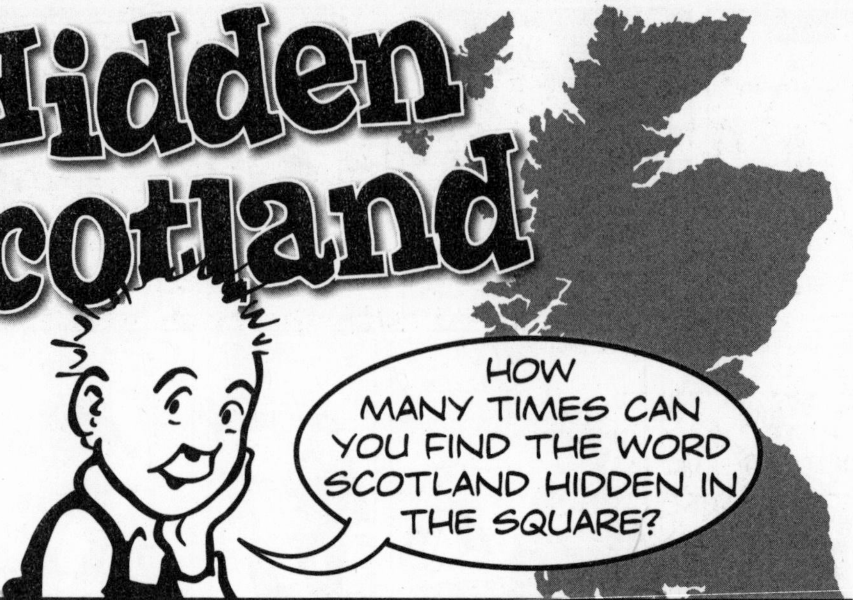

S	N	D	L	O	S	S	S	D	D	S
C	S	A	N	T	C	C	N	D	N	C
O	D	C	C	A	O	A	N	S	A	D
T	S	T	O	T	L	A	D	D	L	N
L	C	O	L	T	L	T	N	O	T	A
A	N	A	O	T	L	A	O	T	O	L
N	N	C	O	A	L	A	L	C	C	T
D	S	C	O	T	L	A	N	D	S	O
L	S	C	O	T	L	A	N	D	O	C
A	D	C	D	N	A	L	T	O	C	S
N	S	C	O	T	L	A	N	D	S	C

ANSWER: 12.

WORDS, WORDS, WORDS

Unscramble the letters in the boxes to find a word associated with Scottish scenery.

```
U N O
A N S
M I T
```

When you have found the word, see how many other words of three letters or more you can make from it. The letter appearing in the black box must appear in all your words.

JUMBLED ISLANDS

ESKY

WELIS

MUR

CKUM

GGIE

Unscramble the groups of letters to find the names of five Scottish islands.

FACE THE MUSIC

STRING

....

....

....

....

....

....

How quickly can you put these musical instruments under the correct heading?

SAXOPHONE
BANJO ZITHER
BASSOON VIOLA
OBOE MANDOLIN
FLUTE LYRE
FIFE CELLO
CLARINET

WIND

....

....

....

....

....

....

HELMETS

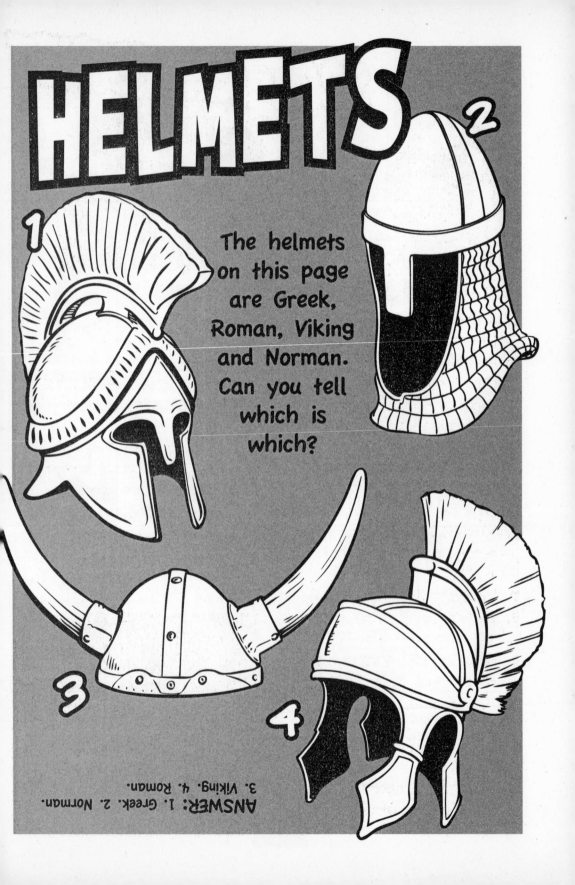

The helmets on this page are Greek, Roman, Viking and Norman. Can you tell which is which?

1

2

3

4

SCOTTISH TOURIST QUIZ

1. Where in Angus is the Reekie Linn waterfall?
   Is it Glen Clova, Glenisla or Glen Prosen?
2. What is Skara Brae?
3. Where is Skara Brae?
4. Where would you go to see the Stone of Destiny?
5. In which river will you see the Bass Rock?
6. Which Scottish attraction became a World Heritage Site in 2001?
7. Where is the Royal Mile?
8. In which Scottish city can you visit Discovery Point?
9. Which monument sits on the Abbey Craig near Stirling?
10. On which island are the Callanish Standing Stones situated – Iona, Mull or Lewis?
11. Abbotsford, near Melrose, was the home of which Scottish writer? Was it Sir Arthur Conan Doyle, Robert Louis Stevenson or Sir Walter Scott?
12. What stretches 95 miles from Milngavie to Fort William?
13. Which part of the coastal area of Scotland is known as the East Neuk?
14. Which famous landmark overlooks Loch Tummel?
15. Urquhart Castle can be found beside which Scottish loch?

COUNTRY QUEST

1. In which country would you find Mount Vesuvius?
2. Which country is famous for its flamenco dancing?
3. The yen is the currency of which country?
4. The Great Barrier Reef can be found off the coast of which country?
5. In which country would you find the cities of Montreal and Toronto?
6. Where is the Grand Canyon?

1 ....
2 ....
3 ....
4 ....
5 ....
6 ....

ANSWERS: 1. ITALY, 2. SPAIN, 3. JAPAN, 4. AUSTRALIA, 5. CANADA, 6. USA.

FAST FOOD MATCH-UP!

How quickly can you match the dishes to their countries of origin?

HAGGIS GAZPACHO

GOULASH SPAGHETTI BOLOGNESE SUSHI

BORSCHT

SAUERKRAUT

COLCANNON

? ? ? ? ? ? ? ? ? ? ? ? ? ?

iRELAND
SPAiN
GERMANY
HUNGARY
JAPAN
SCOTLAND
RUSSIA
iTALY

NAME-MAZE!

Can you find a way along the lines without coming to a dead end? When you've found the right way, write down the letters you pass in the order you come to them and you'll find a boy's name.

START

FINISH

ANSWER: MICHAEL.

?????????????????????

See if you can help Wullie write a different single number in the empty cirles below to make each of the rows add up to 15.

?????????????????????

ANSWER: Top row: 6, 7, 2. Bottom row: 8, 3, 4.

LUCKY NUMBERS

PUT NUMBERS IN THE BLANK BOXES SO THAT EACH LINE ADDS UP TO 21.

	3	6	
5			5
5			6
	9	3	

	4	2	
6			7
4			3
	6	8	

ANSWERS:

A-MAZE-ING!

Can you make it to the finish before the ice-cream melts?

WHY WERE KING ARTHUR'S ARMY TIRED?

BECAUSE THEY HAD TOO MANY LATE KNIGHTS!

OOR WULLIE FUN SECTION

Teacher — "Name the Scottish engineer who invented a steam engine."
Pupil — "What, sir?"
Teacher — "Well done! Watt!"

"Did you ever own a musical instrument?"
"Well, I used to have some drumsticks. . . — but I cooked them and ate them!"

Waiter — "One pound for a cup of coffee, sir, and the refills are free!"
Diner — "I'll just have a refill, then!"

Policeman — "I'm putting you in the cells for the night, mate!"
Criminal — "What's the charge?"
Policeman — "No charge — it's absolutely free!"

WORDSEARCH

Find the things I like and dinny like about school in the wordsearch below.

```
F S Q W V A S R E H C A E T B
R M B A C F E X A M S C L W J
I E A G S H Z N L X I U U Z A
E O R W N E E L E T H G H P N
N P O E E I L A E M N O K I I
D T O T P A L M T I I D Q L T
S M G O B O H L Y I L E I H O
Z T F T T R A E E N N S O R
Q T O U I S L T A P E G M M E
J O G R K P K R S S S P F E A
F Q A C X G N Q V Z K T G W D
H L I R D I S T A R I N G O I
I R A X N N I O S Q W N F R N
T W C G W K I Y U W R E N K G
X T E I A S R E K N O C Q B B
```

ARITHMETIC
CHEATING
CONKERS
ENEMIES
EXAMS
FOOTBALL
FRIENDS
HOMEWORK
JANITOR
LEARNING
LINES
PLAYING
POEMS
READING
REPORTS
SPELLING
STARING
SWOTS
TEACHERS
TRICKS

A   H   O   ?
        ?
                    Y
            G
        ?   ?
    T
    R   S

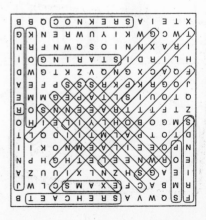

Bright Ideas

PLANTS, BiRDS AND BOXES

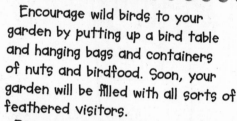

Collect seeds from a selection of local plants or trees.

Next time you are in the countryside, plant them in verges or waste ground.

Your flowers will look super when they start to grow and people will be less likely to dump rubbish there.

Alternatively, you could buy a packet of mixed wild-flower seeds and scatter these around. The seeds you scatter or plant may take some time to grow but the end result will be worthwhile.

Encourage wild birds to your garden by putting up a bird table and hanging bags and containers of nuts and birdfood. Soon, your garden will be filled with all sorts of feathered visitors.

Remember to put out containers of water, too, because the birds will need this in summer and winter.

Birds can also be encouraged to visit your garden if you put up nest boxes for them and you can encourage nocturnal visitors, such as pipistrelle bats, by putting up a bat box.

BOREDOM BUSTERS Skittles

Carefully wash out large plastic drinks bottles then leave upside down to drain and dry. Screw the lids back on and now you're ready to begin painting.

Give each bottle a coat of paint (you might need two), allow to dry, then paint on decoration. When the bottles are dry you can have fun knocking down your skittles.

REMEMBER TAE DRINK THE FIZZY POP BEFORE YOU USE THE BOTTLES!

SPLIT the FIELD

Using only two straight lines, can you divide the field so that there are just two sheep in each section?

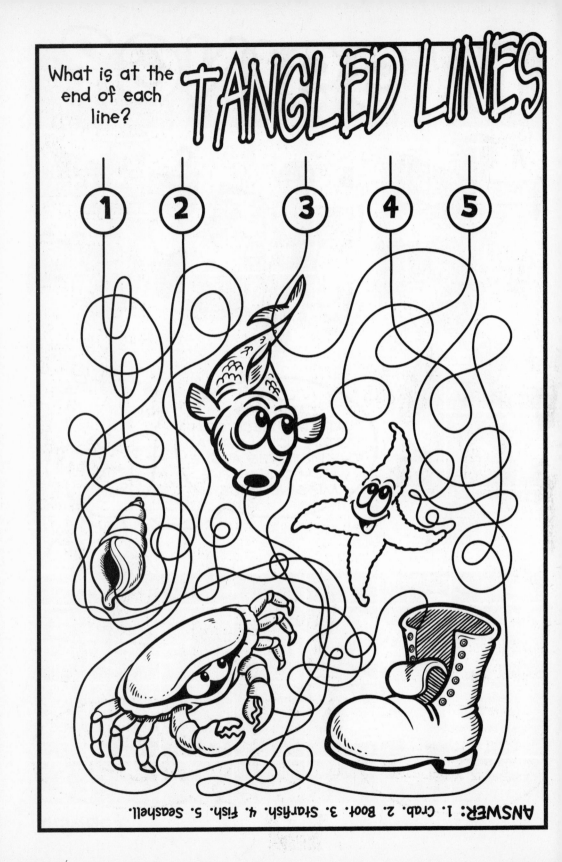

What is at the end of each line?

TANGLED LINES

1   2   3   4   5

ANSWER: 1. Crab. 2. Boot. 3. Starfish. 4. Fish. 5. Seashell.

MISSING?

A

B

C

D

LOOK CAREFULLY AT THIS PIECE OF TARTAN. NOW LOOK AT THE PICTURES ABOVE. WHICH ONE IS THE MISSING PIECE?

ANSWER: C

CHANGE OVER

Here is a number square containing 16 numbers. Can you change the numbers into letters which will form a word square simply by adding 19 short straight lines to them? (In a word square the same words should read both down and across.)

3	O	O	I
O	3	O	I
O	O	7	I
I	I	I	I

LimeRick LaUGHs

A hairy wee dug frae Stranraer,
Loved travelling around in the car!
He'd jump onto the seat,
Wouldn't lie at your feet,
And sleep all the way
to Dunbar.

A gardener from north of Dundee
Starting digging to plant a new tree.
For ten hours or more
He dug through the earth's core,
And landed in Melbourne
for tea.

A keen lady curler from Dyce
Slipped while taking her turn on the ice.
She shot down the rink,
Then said with a wink,
"Stick to bowling greens, that's
my advice!"

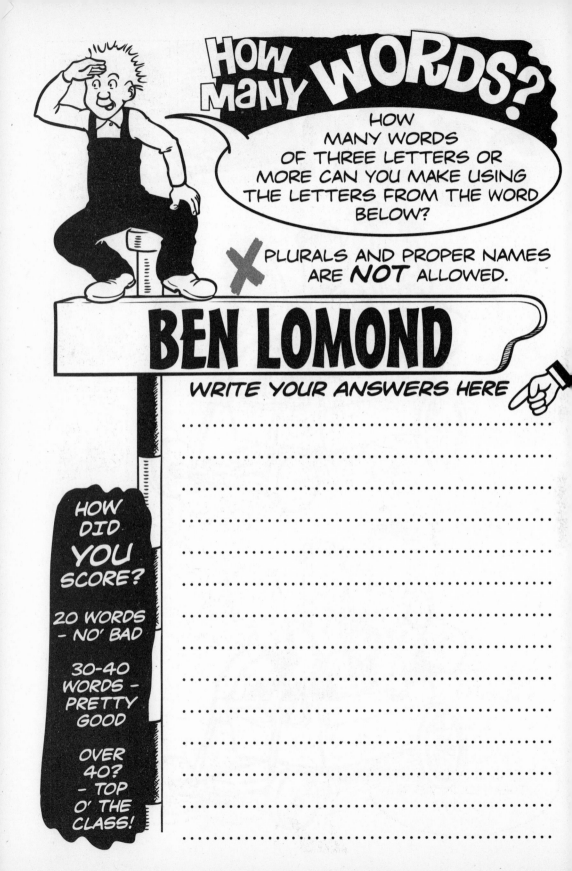

LOOK again

THERE ARE SIX DIFFERENCES BETWEEN THE TWO PICTURES BELOW. **CAN YOU FIND THEM?**

OOR WULLIE® FUN SECTION

1st spider — "I'm famous now!"
2nd spider — "Why do you say that?"
1st spider — "Didn't you see me on the television last night?"

Bill — "I tried to swat a fly that was crawling on the television last night!"
Will — "Did you hit it?"
Bill — "No — but I got it on video!"

Waiter — "Would you like to try some of our bullet salad sir?"
Diner — "I've never heard of such a thing before. Why do you call it that?"
Waiter — "Because there are slugs in it, sir."

Teacher — "What is the least used bone in your body?"
Pupil — "My head!"

FASCINATING FACTS

Even though golf was invented in Scotland, it hasn't always enjoyed a great reputation here. The very first mention of the game is when James II banned people from playing it in 1457, saying they should practise archery instead. It was banned another three times over the next couple of hundred years, and was so looked down upon during Mary Queen of Scots' reign that she was accused of playing it by her political enemies!

A story goes that the Highland Fling developed as a dance performed by victorious Scottish warriors returning home from battle, who would dance on their shields, or targes. These usually had a sharp steel spike in the middle, so the warriors had to use their skill to dance around it, and avoid injuring themselves.

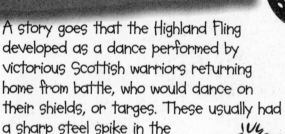

Scotland has the highest proportion of redheads in the world, at around 13%, with 40% carrying the gene that makes people redheads.

From 1st August 1746 until 1782, wearing kilts or tartan was illegal in Scotland. The "Dress Act" was also used to stop people playing bagpipes.

OOR WULLIE'S

The oldest species in the world is thought to be the tadpole shrimp. Fossils of it have been found dating back 200 million years, but colonies of them were recently found alive and well on the Solway Coast.

South Lanarkshire's Hamilton Mausoleum has the longest echo of any man-made structure in the world, lasting for 15 whole seconds!

The record for haggis eating is 1.4kg in 8 minutes, set in America in 2008.

The ancient universities of Scotland traditionally had "Meal Monday" on the second Monday of February, when students could return home to their farms to stock up on oatmeal. It is still observed by St Andrews today.

Margaret, Maid of Norway, was named Queen of Scotland at age 3, but died in Orkney, on her way to Scotland, in 1290, without ever having set foot in the country.

General Tam Dalyell, "Bluidy Tam", is said to have played cards with the devil. On one occasion, he beat the Devil, who, in a rage, threw the card table at him, missing and sending it flying out the window. Visitors to his house, the House of the Binns, today can see the table they are supposed to have played at.

A ♠

QUIZ BIZ!

1. What is the name of the imaginary line around the centre of the earth?

2. **What killed Cleopatra?**

3. What are mammals which have pouches for their young called?

4. **Which rodent has no tail?**

5. Who wrote "A Midsummer Night's Dream"?

6. **How many wives did Henry VIII have?**

7. How many arms does the Venus De Milo statue have?

8. **Where were the Hanging Gardens, one of the Seven Wonders of the Ancient World?**

9. Which city had a "Great Fire" in 1666?

10. **Which bear has the latin name "ursus arctos"?**

ANSWERS

1. The equator.
2. An asp.
3. Marsupials.
4. The guinea pig.
5. William Shakespeare.
6. Six.
7. None.
8. Babylon.
9. London.
10. The brown bear (not the polar!)

HOW MANY WORDS?

HOW MANY WORDS OF THREE LETTERS OR MORE CAN YOU MAKE USING THE LETTERS FROM THIS WORD?

HIGHLANDS

X PLURALS AND PROPER NAMES ARE **NOT** ALLOWED.

WRITE YOUR ANSWERS HERE

....

....

....

....

....

....

....

....

....

HOW DID **YOU** SCORE?

20 WORDS – NO' BAD
30-40 WORDS – PRETTY GOOD
OVER 40? – TOP O' THE CLASS!

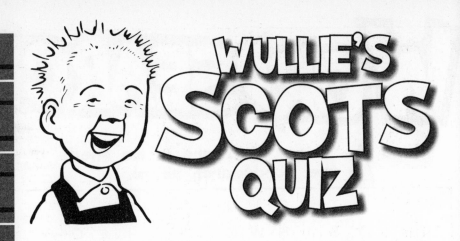

WULLIE'S SCOTS QUIZ

1 The name of which Scottish village reads the same backwards as forwards?

2 Which town on Mull is famous for its colourful houses?

3 Fingal's Cave is on which island in the Hebrides?

4 Which city is regarded as the capital of the Highlands?

5 What is the only "Cape" in Scotland?

6 What are Eigg, Muck, Rùm and Canna?

7 How long is the Southern Upland Way? 2.5 miles, 212 miles or 2012 miles?

8 Which village in Stirling sounds like you might nail it to the wall on the 1st of January?

9 Which river is Dundee on?

10 Which city is known as "The Fair City"?

WORDSEARCH

Find the things that are in ma shed in the wordsearch below.

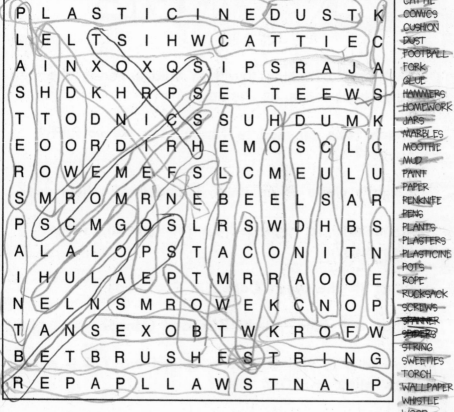

```
P L A S T I C I N E D U S T K
L E L T S I H W C A T T I E C
A I N X O X Q S I P S R A J A
S H D K H R P S E I T E E W S
T T O D N I C S S U H D U M K
E O O R D I R H E M O S C L C
R O W E M E F S L C M E U L U
S M R O M R N E B E E L S A R
P S C M G O S L R S W D H B S
A L A L O P S T A C O N I T N
I H U L A E P T M R R A O O E
N E L N S M R O W E K C N O P
T A N S E X O B T W K R O F W
B E T B R U S H E S T R I N G
R E P A P L L A W S T N A L P
```

A H O ?
? H Y
G
T ? ?
R S

OOR WULLIE

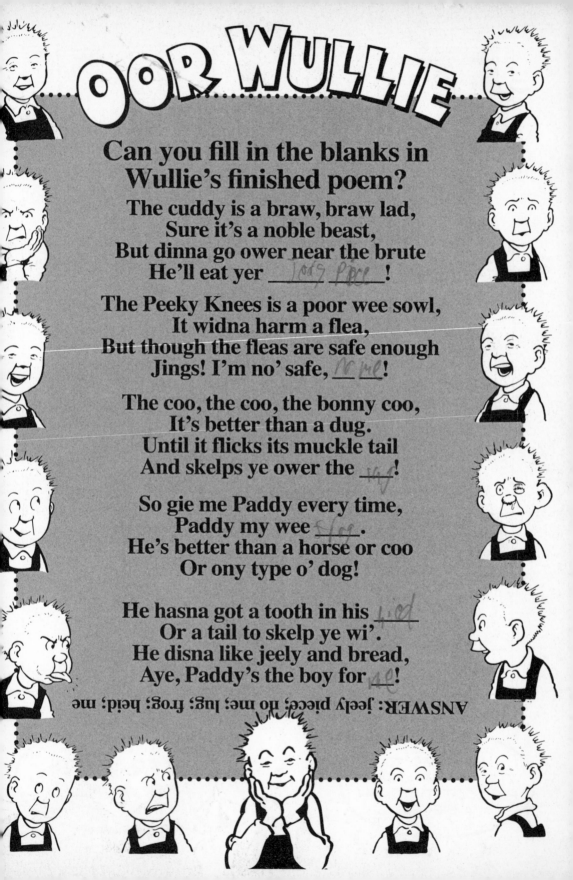

Can you fill in the blanks in Wullie's finished poem?

The cuddy is a braw, braw lad,
Sure it's a noble beast,
But dinna go ower near the brute
He'll eat yer _____ jeely piece_____!

The Peeky Knees is a poor wee sowl,
It widna harm a flea,
But though the fleas are safe enough
Jings! I'm no' safe, _no me_!

The coo, the coo, the bonny coo,
It's better than a dug.
Until it flicks its muckle tail
And skelps ye ower the _lug_!

So gie me Paddy every time,
Paddy my wee _frog_.
He's better than a horse or coo
Or ony type o' dog!

He hasna got a tooth in his _heid_
Or a tail to skelp ye wi'.
He disna like jeely and bread,
Aye, Paddy's the boy for _me_!

ANSWER: jeely piece; no me; lug; frog; heid; me